CLASSIC
POETRY
FOR CHILDREN

INTRODUCTION

In this collection of well-loved poems, you will see amazing sights, meet strange and spooky people and read words that may make you sing, dance and even cry.

Poets use words in a special way. They seem to be able to squeeze lots of meanings and feelings into just a few lines. Sometimes it is hard to understand everything the poet is saying. That may be because a poem was written long ago or uses a kind of English that is unlike the language you speak. Don't worry if you can't understand everything. Poems can surprise and please you each time you read them, as you understand a little more each time.

It is always a good idea to try reading a poem aloud. Some odd words make sense as soon as you say them. And even if parts of the poem sound strange and mysterious, you will be able to hear the rhythm and rhyme of the lines, which is just what the poet wanted you to do.

At the end of the book, you will find a glossary of the most difficult words of all—the ones I had to look up in a dictionary, too! There is also some information about the poets and an index of titles and first lines, so it will always be easy for you to find the poems you like best and read them over and over again!

N.M.A.B.

CLASSIC
POETRY
FOR CHILDREN

Illustrated by Cathie Shuttleworth
Compiled by Nicola Baxter

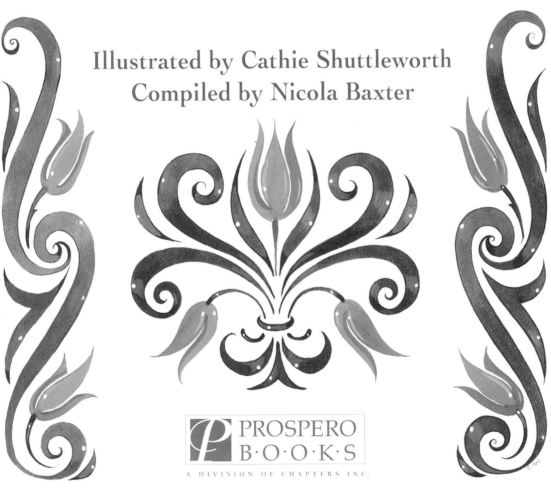

PROSPERO
B·O·O·K·S
A DIVISION OF CHAPTERS INC.

THIS EDITION PRODUCED FOR PROSPERO BOOKS
A DIVISION OF CHAPTERS INC

© 2000 Bookmart Limited

Published by Armadillo Books
an imprint of
Bookmart Limited
Registered Number 2372865
Trading as Bookmart Limited
Desford Road
Enderby
Leicester
LE9 5AD

ISBN 1-55267-306-5

Produced for Bookmart Limited by
Nicola Baxter
PO Box 215
Framingham Earl
Norwich
NR14 7UR

Designed by Amanda Hawkes

Printed in Italy

CONTENTS

LOVE AND ADVENTURE

Robin Hood	8
A Red, Red, Rose	10
A Birthday	11
Lochinvar	12
A New Courtly Sonnet of the Lady Greensleeves	14
The Night Has a Thousand Eyes	16

SONGS AND BALLADS

Thomas the Rhymer	18
Bonny Barbara Allan	22
The Great Silkie of Sule Skerrie	24
The Yarn of the *Nancy Bell*	26

BOYS AND GIRLS

What Am I After All	32
Jemima	33
There Was a Naughty Boy	34
The False Knight and the Wee Boy	36
Children	38
When That I Was and a Little Tiny Boy	40

MAGIC AND MYSTERY

Waltzing Matilda	42
The Ghost's Song	43
John Barleycorn	44
A Strange Visitor	47
The Oxen	50

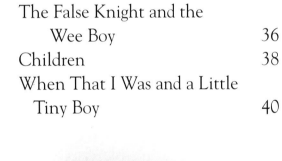

SIGHTS AND SOUNDS

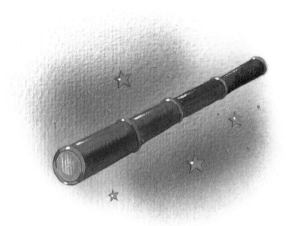

Upon Westminster Bridge   52
On First Looking into
        Chapman's Homer   53
Symphony in Yellow   54
A Thing of Beauty   55
From The Garden   56

SADNESS AND HAPPINESS

So, We'll Go No More
        A-Roving   64
Spring and Fall   65
Canadian Boat Song   66
In the Highlands   68
When in Disgrace With
        Fortune   69
Piping Down the Valleys Wild   70
A Lark's Nest   71
From The Song of Solomon   71
The Swing   72
Requiem   73

About the Poets   74

Glossary   77

Index of Titles and First Lines   79

MUSIC AND DANCING

Song's Eternity   58
Music   60
Piano   61
I am of Ireland   62
To Emilia V—   62

LOVE and ADVENTURE

Robin Hood

In Sherwood lived stout Robin Hood,
    An Archer great none greater.
His bow and shafts were sure and good,
    Yet Cupid's were much better.
Robin could shoot at many a Hart and miss,
    Cupid at first could hit a heart of his.
        Hey jolly Robin,
        Hoe jolly Robin,
        Hey jolly Robin Hood,
        Love finds out me
        As well as thee
        To follow me to the green wood.

A noble thief was Robin Hood,
     Wise was he could deceive him,
Yet Marian in his bravest mood
     Could of his heart bereave him,
No greater thief lies hidden under skies
     Than beauty closely lodged in women's eyes.
          Hey jolly Robin,
          Hoe jolly Robin,
          Hey jolly Robin Hood,
          Love finds out me
          As well as thee
          To follow me to the green wood.

Robert Jones

A Red, Red Rose

My love is like a red, red rose
    That's newly sprung in June:
My love is like the melody
    That's sweetly played in tune.

As fair art thou, my bonnie lass,
    So deep in love am I:
And I will love thee still, my dear,
    Till a' the seas gang dry.

Till a' the seas gang dry, my dear,
    And the rocks melt wi' the sun:
And I will love thee still, my dear,
    While the sands o' life shall run.

And fare thee weel, my only love,
    And fare thee weel a while!
And I will come again, my love,
    Thou' it were ten thousand mile.

Robert Burns

A Birthday

My heart is like a singing bird
    Whose nest is in a watered shoot;
My heart is like an apple-tree
    Whose boughs are bent with thickset fruit;
My heart is like a rainbow shell
    That paddles in a halcyon sea;
My heart is gladder than all these
    Because my love is come to me.

Raise me a dais of silk and down;
    Hang it with vair and purple dyes;
Carve it in doves and pomegranates,
    And peacocks with a hundred eyes;
Work it in gold and silver grapes,
    In leaves and silver fleurs-de-lys;
Because the birthday of my life
    Is come, my love is come to me.

Christina Rossetti

11

Lochinvar

O, young Lochinvar is come out of the west,
Through all the wide Border his steed was the best;
And save his good broadsword he weapons had none,
He rode all unarmed, and he rode all alone.
So faithful in love, and so dauntless in war,
There never was knight like the young Lochinvar.

He stayed not for brake, and he stopped not for stone,
He swam the Eske river where ford there was none;
But ere he alighted at Netherby gate,
The bride had consented, the gallant came late:
For a laggard in love, and a dastard in war,
Was to wed the fair Ellen of brave Lochinvar.

So boldly he entered the Netherby Hall,
Among bride's-men, and kinsmen, and brothers, and all:
Then spoke the bride's father, his hand on his sword,
(For the poor craven bridegroom said never a word)
"O come ye in peace here, or come ye in war,
Or to dance at our bridal, young Lord Lochinvar?"

"I long wooed your daughter, my suit you denied;—
Love swells like the Solway, but ebbs like its tide—
And now am I come, with this lost love of mine,
To lead but one measure, drink one cup of wine.
There are maidens in Scotland more lovely by far,
That would gladly be bride to the young Lochinvar."

12

The bride kissed the goblet: the knight took it up,
He quaffed off the wine, and he threw down the cup.
She looked down to blush, and she looked up to sigh,
With a smile on her lips, and a tear in her eye.
He took her soft hand, ere her mother could bar,—
"Now tread we a measure!" said the young Lochinvar.

So stately his form and so lovely her face,
That never a hall such a galliard did grace;
While her mother did fret, and her father did fume,
And the bridegroom stood dangling his bonnet and plume;
And the bride-maidens whispered, "'Twere better by far,
To have matched our fair cousin with young Lochinvar."

One touch to her hand, and one word in her ear,
When they reached the hall-door, and the charger stood near;
So light to the croup the fair lady he swung,
So light to the saddle before her he sprung!
"She is won! we are gone, over bank, bush, and scaur;
They'll have fleet steeds that follow," quoth young Lochinvar.

There was mounting 'mong Graemes of the Netherby clan;
Forsters, Fenwicks, and Musgraves, they rode and they ran:
There was racing and chasing on Cannobie Lee,
But the lost bride of Netherby n'er did they see.
So daring in love, and so dauntless in war,
Have ye e'er heard of gallant like young Lochinvar?

Sir Walter Scott

A New Courtly Sonnet of the Lady Greensleeves

Alas, my Love! ye do me wrong
To cast me off discourteously;
And I have loved you so long,
Delighting in your company.
    Greensleeves was all my joy,
    Greensleeves was my delight;
    Greensleeves was my heart of gold,
    And who but my Lady Greensleeves.

 I have been ready at your hand,
To grant whatever you would crave;
I have both waged life and land,
Your love and goodwill for to have.

I bought thee kerchers to thy head,
That were wrought fine and gallantly;
I kept thee both at board and bed,
Which cost my purse well favouredly.

I bought thee petticoats of the best,
The cloth so fine as fine might be;
I gave thee jewels for thy chest,
And all this cost I spent on thee.

Thy purse and eke thy gay gild knives,
Thy pincase gallant to the eye;
No better wore the burgess wives,
And yet thou wouldst not love me.

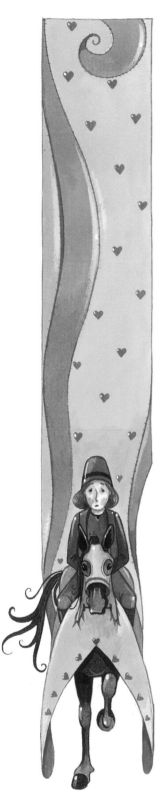

Thy gown was of the grassy green,
Thy sleeves of satin hanging by,
Which made thee be our harvest queen,
And yet thou wouldst not love me.

My gayest gelding I thee gave,
To ride wherever liked thee;
No lady ever was so brave,
And yet thou wouldst not love me.

My men were clothed all in green,
And they did ever wait on thee;
All this was gallant to be seen,
And yet thou wouldst not love me.

For every morning when thou rose,
I sent thee dainties orderly,
To cheer thy stomach from all woes,
And yet thou wouldst not love me.

Well, I will pray to God on high,
That thou my constancy mayst see,
And that yet once before I die,
Thou wilt vouchsafe to love me.

Greensleeves, now farewell! adieu!
God I pray to prosper thee;
For I am still thy lover true.
Come once again and love me.
    Greensleeves was all my joy, etc.

Anonymous,
but some say
King Henry VIII

15

The Night Has a Thousand Eyes

The night has a thousand eyes,
   And the day but one;
Yet the light of the bright world dies
   With the dying sun.

The mind has a thousand eyes,
   And the heart but one;
Yet the light of a whole life dies
   When love is done.

Francis William Bourdillon

SONGS
and
BALLADS

Thomas the Rhymer

True Thomas lay o'er yond grassy bank,
    And he beheld a ladie gay,
A ladie that was brisk and bold,
    Come riding o'er the fernie brae.

Her skirt was of the grass-green silk,
    Her mantel of the velvet fine,
At ilka tett of her horse's mane
    Hung fifty silver bells and nine.

True Thomas he took off his hat,
    And bowed him low down till his knee:
All hail, thou mighty Queen of Heaven!
    For your peer on earth I never did see.

O no, O no, True Thomas, she says,
    That name does not belong to me;
I am but the queen of fair Elfland,
    And I'm come here for to visit thee.

But ye maun go wi' me now, Thomas,
    True Thomas, ye maun go wi' me,
For ye maun serve me seven years,
    Thro weel or wae as may chance to be.

She turned about her milk-white steed,
    And took True Thomas up behind,
And aye whene'er her bridle rang,
    The steed flew swifter than the wind.

O they rade on, and further on,
    Until they came to a garden green:
Light down, light down, ye ladie free,
    Some of that fruit let me pull to thee.

O no, O no, True Thomas, she says,
    That fruit maun not be touched by thee,
For a' the plagues that are in hell
    Light on the fruit of this countrie.

But I have a loaf here in my lap,
    Likewise a bottle of claret wine,
And now ere we go farther on,
    We'll rest a while, and ye may dine.

When he had eaten and drunk his fill,
    Lay down your head upon my knee,
The lady sayd, ere we climb yon hill,
    And I will show you fairlies three.

O see not ye yon narrow road,
    So thick beset wi' thorns and briers?
That is the path of righteousness,
    Tho after it but few enquires.

And see not ye that braid braid road,
    That lies across yon lillie leven?
That is the path of wickedness,
    Tho some call it the road to heaven.

And see not ye that bonny road,
    Which winds about the fernie brae?
That is the road to fair Elfland,
    Where you and I this night maun gae.

But Thomas, ye maun hold your tongue,
    Whatever you may hear or see,
For gin ae word you should chance to speak,
    You will ne'er get back to your ain countrie.

For forty days and forty nights
    He wade thro red blude to the knee,
And he saw neither sun nor moon,
    But heard the roaring of the sea.

He has gotten a coat of the even cloth,
    And a pair of shoes of velvet green,
And till seven years were past and gone
    True Thomas on earth was never seen.

Anonymous

Bonny Barbara Allan

It was in and about the Martinmas time,
    When the green leaves were a-falling,
That Sir John Graeme in the West Country
    Fell in love with Barbara Allan.

He sent his man down through the town,
    To the place where she was dwelling,
O haste, and come to my master dear,
    Gin ye be Barbara Allan.

O hooly, hooly rose she up,
    To the place where he was lying,
And when she drew the curtain by,
    Young man, I think you're dying.

O it's I'm sick, and very very sick,
    And 'tis a' for Barbara Allan,
O the better for me ye's never be,
    Tho your heart's blood were a-spilling.

O dinna ye mind, young man, said she,
    When ye was in the tavern a-drinking,
That ye made the healths gae round and round,
    And slighted Barbara Allan?

He turned his face unto the wall,
    And death was with him dealing;
Adieu, adieu, my dear friends all,
    And be kind to Barbara Allan.

And slowly, slowly raise she up,
    And slowly, slowly left him;
And sighing, said, she could not stay,
    Since death of life had reft him.

She had not gane a mile but twa,
    When she heard the dead-bell ringing,
And every jow that the dead-bell gied,
    It cry'd, Woe to Barbara Allan.

O mother, mother, make my bed,
    O make it saft and narrow,
Since my love died for me today,
    I'll die for him tomorrow.

Anonymous

The Great Silkie of Sule Skerrie

An earthly nourris sits and sings,
    And aye she sings, Ba, lily wean!
Little ken I my bairn's father,
    Far less the land that he staps in.

Then ane arose at her bed-fit,
    An' a grumly guest I'm sure was he:
Here am I, thy bairn's father,
    Although that I be not comelie.

I am a man, upon the land,
    An' I am a silkie in the sea,
And when I'm far and far frae land,
    My dwelling is in Sule Skerry.

24

It was na weel, quo' the maiden fair,
    It was na weel, indeed, quo' she,
That the Great Silkie of Sule Skerry
    Should hae come and aught a bairn to me.

Now he has ta'en a purse of goud,
    And he has put it upo' her knee,
Sayin', Gie to me my little young son,
    An' tak thee up they nourrice-fee.

An' it sall pass on a summer's day,
    When the sun shines het on evera stane,
That I will tak my little young son,
    An' teach him for to swim the faem.

An' thu sall marry a proud gunner,
    An' a proud gunner I'm sure he'll be,
An' the very first shot that ere he shoots,
    He'll shoot baith my young son and me.

Anonymous

The Yarn of the Nancy Bell

'Twas on the shores that round our coast
    From Deal to Ramsgate span,
That I found alone on a piece of stone
    An elderly naval man.

His hair was weedy, his beard was long,
    And weedy and long was he,
And I heard this wight on the shore recite,
    In a singular minor key:

"Oh, I am a cook and a captain bold,
    And the mate of the *Nancy* brig,
And a bo'sun tight, and a midshipmite,
    And the crew of the captain's gig."

And he shook his fists and he tore his hair,
    Till I really felt afraid,
For I couldn't help thinking the man had been drinking,
    And so I simply said:

"Oh, elderly man, it's little I know
    Of the duties of men of the sea,
And I'll eat my hand if I understand
    How you can possibly be

"At once a cook, and a captain bold,
    And the mate of the *Nancy* brig,
And a bo'sun tight, and a midshipmite,
    And the crew of the captain's gig."

Then he gave a hitch to his trousers, which
    Is a trick all seamen larn,
And having got rid of a thumping quid,
    He spun this painful yarn:

"'Twas in the good ship *Nancy Bell*
    That we sailed to the Indian sea
And there on a reef we come to grief,
    Which has often occurred to me.

"And pretty nigh all o' the crew was drowned
    (There was seventy-seven o' soul),
And only ten of the *Nancy's* men
    Said 'Here!' to the muster-roll.

"There was me and the cook and the captain bold,
    And the mate of the *Nancy* brig,
And a bo'sun tight, and a midshipmite,
    And the crew of the captain's gig.

"For a month we'd neither wittles nor drink,
    Till a-hungry we did feel,
So we drawed a lot, and accordin' shot
    The captain for our meal.

"The next lot fell to the *Nancy's* mate,
    And a delicate dish he made;
Then our appetite with the midshipmite
    We seven survivors stayed.

"And then we murdered the bo'sun tight,
    And he much resembled pig;
Then we wittled free, did the cook and me,
    On the crew of the captain's gig.

"Then only the cook and me was left,
    And the delicate question, 'Which
Of us two goes to the kettle?' arose,
    And we argued it out as sich.

"For I loved that cook as a brother, I did,
    And the cook he worshipped me;
But we'd both be blowed if we'd either be stowed
    In the other chap's hold, you see.

"'I'll be eat if you dines off me,' says Tom,
    'Yes, that,' says I, 'you'll be,'—
'I'm boiled if I die, my friend,' quoth I,
    And 'Exactly so,' quoth he.

"Says he, 'Dear James, to murder me
    Were a foolish thing to do,
For don't you see that you can't cook *me*,
    While I can—and will—cook *you!*'

"So he boils the water, and takes the salt
    And the pepper in portions true
(Which he never forgot), and some chopped shallot,
    And some sage and parsley too.

"'Come here,' says he, with a proper pride,
    Which his smiling features tell,
''Twill soothing be if I let you see
    How extremely nice you'll smell.'

"And he stirred it round and round and round,
    And he sniffed at the foaming froth;
When I ups with his heels, and smothers his squeals
    In the scum of the boiling broth.

"And I eat that cook in a week or less,
    And—as I eating be
The last of his chops, why, I almost drops,
    For a wessel in sight I see!

"And I never larf, and I never smile,
    And I never lark nor play,
But I sit and croak, and a single joke
    I have—which is to say:

"Oh, I am a cook and a captain bold,
    And the mate of the *Nancy* brig,
And a bo'sun tight, and a midshipmite,
    And the crew of the captain's gig!"

Sir W. S. Gilbert

Boys and Girls

What Am I After All

What am I after all but a child, pleas'd with the sound of
    my own name? repeating it over and over;
I stand apart to hear—it never tires me.

To you your name also;
Did you think there was nothing but two or three
    pronunciations in the sound of your name?

Walt Whitman

Jemima

There was a little girl, and she wore a little curl
    Right down the middle of her forehead,
When she was good, she was very, very, good,
    But when she was bad, she was horrid!

One day she went upstairs, while her parents, unawares,
    In the kitchen down below were occupied with meals,
And she stood upon her head, on her little truckle bed,
    And she then began hurraying with her heels.

Her mother heard the noise, and thought it was the boys
    A-playing at a combat in the attic,
But when she climbed the stair and saw Jemima there,
    She took and she did whip her most emphatic.

Anonymous

There Was a Naughty Boy

There was a naughty Boy
    A naughty Boy was he
He would not stop at home
He could not quiet be—
    He took
    In his Knapsack
    A Book
    Full of vowels
    And a shirt
    With some towels—
    A slight cap
    For night cap—
    A hair brush
    Comb ditto
    New Stockings
    For old ones
    Would split O!
    This Knapsack
    Tight at's back
    He rivetted close
And follow'd his Nose
    To the North
    To the North
And follow'd his Nose
    To the North.

There was a naughty Boy
    And a naughty Boy was he
He ran away to Scotland
    The people for to see—
        There he found
        That the ground
        Was as hard
        That a yard
        Was as long,
        That a song
        Was as merry,
        That a cherry
        Was as red—
        That lead
        Was as weighty
        That forescore
        Was as eighty
        That a door
        Was as wooden
        As in England—
        So he stood in
        His shoes
        And he wonder'd
        He stood in his
        Shoes and he wonder'd.

John Keats

35

The False Knight and the Wee Boy

"O whare are ye gaun?"
  Quo' the fause knicht upon the road:
"I'm gaun to the scule,"
  Quo' the wee boy, and still he stude.

"What is that upon your back?"
  Quo' the fause knicht upon the road:
"Atweel it is my bukes,"
  Quo' the wee boy, and still he stude.

"Wha's aucht thae sheep?"
  Quo' the fause knicht upon the road:
"They are mine and my mither's,"
  Quo' the wee boy, and still he stude.

"How mony o' them are mine?"
  Quo' the fause knicht upon the road:
"A' they that hae blue tails,"
  Quo' the wee boy, and still he stude.

"I wiss ye were on yon tree,"
  Quo' the fause knicht upon the road:
"And for you to fa' down,"
  Quo' the wee boy, and still he stude.

"I wiss ye were in yon sie,"
  Quo' the fause knicht upon the road:
"And a gude bottom under me,"
  Quo' the wee boy, and still he stude.

"And the bottom for to break,"
    Quo' the fause knicht upon the road:
"*And ye to be drowned,*"
    Quo' the wee boy, and still he stude.

Anonymous

Children

Come to me, O ye children!
    For I hear you at your play,
And the questions that perplexed me
    Have vanished quite away.

Ye open the eastern windows,
    That look towards the sun,
Where thoughts are singing swallows
    And the brooks of morning run.

In your hearts are the birds and the sunshine,
    In your thoughts the brooklet's flow,
But in mine is the wind of Autumn
    And the first fall of the snow.

Ah! what would the world be to us
    If the children were no more?
We should dread the desert behind us
    Worse than the dark before.

What the leaves are to the forest,
    With light and air for food,
Ere their sweet and tender juices
    Have been hardened into wood,—

That to the world are children;
    Through them it feels the glow
Of a brighter and sunnier climate
    Than reaches the trunks below.

Come to me, O ye children!
And whisper in my ear
What the birds and the winds are singing
    In your sunny atmosphere.

For what are all our contrivings,
    And the wisdom of our books,
What compared with your caresses,
    And the gladness of your looks?

Ye are better than all the ballads
    That ever were sung or said;
For ye are living poems,
    And all the rest are dead.

Henry Wadsworth Longfellow

When That I Was and a Little Tiny Boy

When that I was and a little tiny boy,
    With hey, ho, the wind and the rain;
A foolish thing was but a toy,
    For the rain it raineth every day.

For when I came to man's estate,
    With hey, ho, the wind and the rain;
'Gainst knaves and thieves men shut their gate,
    For the rain it raineth every day.

But when I came, alas! to wive,
    With hey, ho, the wind and the rain;
By swaggering could I never thrive,
    For the rain it raineth every day.

But when I came unto my beds,
    With hey, ho, the wind and the rain;
With toss-pots still had drunken heads,
    For the rain it raineth every day.

A great while ago the world begun,
    With hey, ho, the wind and the rain;
But that's all one, our play is done,
    And we'll strive to please you every day.

William Shakespeare

MAGIC and MYSTERY

Waltzing Matilda

Once a jolly swagman camped by a billabong,
　　Under the shade of a coolabah tree;
And he sang as he watched and waited till his billy boiled,
　　"You'll come a-waltzing Matilda with me!"

"Waltzing Matilda, Waltzing Matilda,
　　You'll come a-waltzing Matilda with me,"
And he sang as he watched and waited till his billy boiled,
　　"You'll come a-waltzing Matilda with me."

Down came a jumbuck to drink at the billabong,
　　Up jumped the swagman and grabbed him with glee;
And he sang as he shoved that jumbuck in his tucker-bag,
　　"You'll come a-waltzing Matilda with me."

"Waltzing Matilda, Waltzing Matilda,
　　You'll come a-waltzing Matilda with me,"
And he sang as he shoved that jumbuck in his tucker-bag,
　　"You'll come a-waltzing Matilda with me."

Up rode the squatter mounted on his thoroughbred;
　　Down came the troopers—one, two and three.
"Whose the jolly jumbuck you've got in your tucker-bag?
　　You'll come a-waltzing Matilda with me."

"Waltzing Matilda, Waltzing Matilda,
　　You'll come a-waltzing Matilda with me,
Whose the jolly jumbuck you've got in your tucker-bag?
　　You'll come a-waltzing Matilda with me."

Up jumped the swagman, sprang into the billabong,
"You'll never catch me alive," said he.
And his ghost may be heard as you pass by that billabong,
"Who'll come a-waltzing Matilda with me?"

"Waltzing Matilda, Waltzing Matilda,
You'll come a-waltzing Matilda with me,"
And his ghost may be heard as you pass by that billabong,
"Who'll come a-waltzing Matilda with me?"

A. B. Paterson

The Ghost's Song

Wae's me! wae's me!
The acorn's not yet
Fallen from the tree
That's to grow the wood,
That's to make the cradle,
That's to rock the bairn,
That's to grow a man,
That's to lay me.

Anonymous

43

John Barleycorn

There was three Kings into the east,
   Three Kings both great and high,
And they hae sworn a solemn oath
   John Barleycorn should die.

They took a plough and plough'd him down,
   Put clods upon his head,
And they hae sworn a solemn oath
   John Barleycorn was dead.

But the cheerfu' Spring came kindly on,
   And show'rs began to fall;
John Barleycorn got up again,
   And sore surprised them all.

The sultry suns of Summer came,
   And he grew thick and strong,
His head weel arm'd wi' pointed spears,
   That no one should him wrong.

The sober Autumn enter'd mild,
   When he grew wan and pale;
His bending joints and drooping head
   Show'd he began to fail.

His colour sicken'd more and more,
   He faded into age;
And then his enemies began
   To shew their deadly rage.

They've ta'en a weapon, long and sharp,
 And cut him by the knee;
Then tied him fast upon a cart,
 Like a rogue for forgerie.

They laid him down upon his back,
 And cudgell'd him full sore;
They hung him up before the storm,
 And turn'd him o'er and o'er.

They filled up a darksome pit
 With water to the brim,
They heaved in John Barleycorn,
 There let him sink or swim.

They laid him out upon the floor,
 To work him farther woe,
And still, as signs of life appear'd,
 They toss'd him to and fro.

They wasted, o'er a scorching flame,
 The marrow of his bones;
But a miller us'd him worst of all,
 For he crush'd him between two stones.

And they hae ta'en his very heart's blood,
 And drank it round and round;
And still the more and more they drank,
 Their joy did more abound.

45

John Barleycorn was a hero bold,
    Of noble enterprise,
For if you do but taste his blood,
    'Twill make your courage rise;

'Twill make a man forget his woe;
    'Twill heighten all his joy:
'Twill make the widow's heart to sing,
    Tho' the tear were in her eye.

Then let us toast John Barleycorn,
    Each man a glass in hand;
And may his great posterity
    Ne'er fail in old Scotland!

Robert Burns

A Strange Visitor

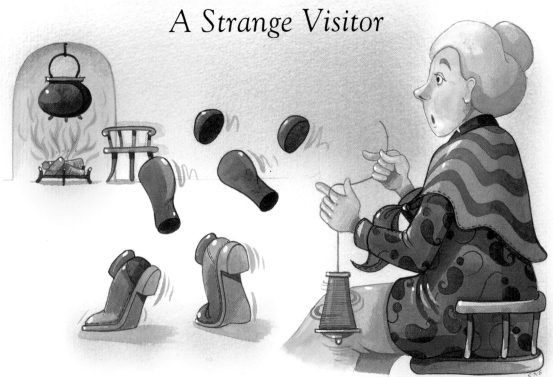

A wife was sitting at her reel ae night;
And aye she sat, and aye she reeled, and aye she wished for company.

In came a pair o' braid braid soles, and sat down at the fireside;
And aye she sat, and aye she reeled, and aye she wished for company.

In came a pair o' sma' sma' legs, and sat down on the braid braid soles;
And aye she sat, and aye she reeled, and aye she wished for company.

In came a pair o' muckle muckle knees, and sat down on the sma' sma' legs;
And aye she sat, and aye she reeled, and aye she wished for company.

In came a pair o' sma' sma' thees, and sat down on the muckle muckle knees;
And aye she sat, and aye she reeled, and aye she wished for company.

In came a pair o' muckle muckle hips, and sat down on the sma' sma' thees;
And aye she sat, and aye she reeled, and aye she wished for company.

In came a sma' sma' waist, and sat down on the muckle muckle hips;
And aye she sat, and aye she reeled, and aye she wished for company.

In came a pair o' braid braid shouthers, and sat down on the sma' sma' waist;
And aye she sat, and aye she reeled, and aye she wished for company.

In came a pair o' sma' sma' arms, and sat down on the braid braid shouthers;
And aye she sat, and aye she reeled, and aye she wished for company.

In came a pair o' muckle muckle hands, and sat down on the sma' sma' arms;
And aye she sat, and aye she reeled, and aye she wished for company.

In came a sma' sma' neck, and sat down on the braid braid shouthers;
And aye she sat, and aye she reeled, and aye she wished for company.

In came a great big head, and sat down on the sma' sma' neck;
And aye she sat, and aye she reeled, and aye she wished for company.

48

"What way hae ye sic braid braid feet?" quo' the wife.
"Muckle ganging, muckle ganging."
"What way hae ye sic sma' sma' legs?"
"*Aih-h-h!*—late—and *wee-e-e* moul."
"What way hae ye sic muckle muckle knees?"
"Muckle praying, muckle praying."
"What way hae ye sic sma' sma' thees?"
"*Aih-h-h!*—late—and *wee-e-e* moul."
"What way hae ye sic big big hips?"
"Muckle sitting, muckle sitting."
"What way hae ye sic a sma' sma' waist?"
"*Aih-h-h!*—late—and *wee-e-e* moul."
"What way hae ye sic braid braid shouthers?"
"Wi' carying broom, wi' carrying broom."
"What way hae ye sic sma' sma' arms?"
"*Aih-h-h!*—late—and *wee-e-e* moul."
"What way hae ye sic muckle muckle hands?"
"Threshing wi' an iron flail, threshing wi' an iron flail."
"What way hae ye sic a sma' sma' neck?"
"*Aih-h-h!*—late—and *wee-e-e* moul."
"What way hae ye sic a muckle muckle head?"
"Muckle wit, muckle wit."
"What do you come for?"
"For YOU!"

Anonymous

49

The Oxen

Christmas Eve, and twelve of the clock.
    "Now they are all on their knees,"
An elder said as we sat in a flock
    By the embers in hearthside ease.

We pictured the meek mild creatures where
    They dwelt in their strawy pen,
Nor did it occur to one of us there
    To doubt they were kneeling then.

So fair a fancy few would weave
    In these years! Yet, I feel,
If someone said on Christmas Eve,
    "Come; see the oxen kneel,

"In the lonely barton by yonder coomb
    Our childhood used to know,"
I should go with him in the gloom,
    Hoping it might be so.

Thomas Hardy

SIGHTS
and
SOUNDS

Upon Westminster Bridge

Earth has nothing to show more fair:
Dull would he be of soul who could pass by
A sight so touching in its majesty:
This City now doth, like a garment, wear
The beauty of the morning; silent, bare,
Ships, towers, domes, theatres, and temples lie
Open unto the fields, and to the sky;
All bright and glittering in the smokeless air.
Never did sun more beautifully steep
In his first splendour, valley, rock, or hill;
Ne'er saw I, never felt, a calm so deep!
The river glideth at his own sweet will:
Dear God! the very houses seem asleep;
And all that mighty heart is lying still!

William Wordsworth

On First Looking into Chapman's Homer

Much have I travell'd in the realms of gold,
    And many goodly states and kingdoms seen;
    Round many western islands have I been
Which bards in fealty to Apollo hold.
    That deep-brow'd Homer ruled as his demesne;
    Yet did I never breathe its pure serene
Till I heard Chapman speak out loud and bold:
Then felt I like some watcher of the skies
    When a new planet swims into his ken;
Or like stout Cortez when with eagle eyes
    He star'd at the Pacific—and all his men
Look'd at each other with a wild surmise—
    Silent, upon a peak in Darien.

John Keats

53

Symphony in Yellow

An omnibus across the bridge
Crawls like a yellow butterfly,
And, here and there, a passer-by
Shows like a little restless midge.

Big barges full of yellow hay
Are moored against the shadowy wharf,
And, like a yellow silken scarf,
The thick fog hangs along the quay.

The yellow leaves begin to fade
And flutter from the Temple elms,
And at my feet the pale green Thames
Lies like a rod of rippled jade.

Oscar Wilde

A Thing of Beauty

A thing of beauty is a joy for ever:
Its loveliness increases; it will never
Pass into nothingness; but still will keep
A bower quiet for us, and a sleep
Full of sweet dreams, and health, and quiet breathing.
Therefore, on every morrow, are we wreathing
A flowery band to bind us to the earth,
Spite of despondence, of the inhuman death
Of noble natures, of the gloomy days,
Of all the unhealthy and o'er-darkened ways
Made for our searching: yes, in spite of all,
Some shape of beauty moves away the pall
From our dark spirits.

John Keats

From *The Garden*

What wondrous life in this I lead!
Ripe apples drop about my head;
The luscious clusters of the vine
Upon my mouth do crush their wine;
The nectarine, and curious peach,
Into my hands themselves do reach;
Stumbling on melons, as I pass,
Ensnared with flowers, I fall on grass.

Meanwhile the mind, from pleasure less,
Withdraws into its happiness:
The mind, that ocean where each kind
Does straight its own resemblance find;
Yet it creates, transcending these,
Far other worlds, and other seas;
Annihilating all that's made
To a green thought in a green shade.

Andrew Marvell

MUSIC
and
DANCING

Song's Eternity

What is song's eternity?
    Come and see.
Can it noise and bustle be?
    Come and see.
Praises sung or praises said
    Can it be?
Wait awhile and these are dead—
    Sigh—sigh;
Be they high or lowly bred
    They die.

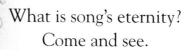

What is song's eternity?
    Come and see.
Melodies of earth and sky,
    Here they be.
Song once sung to Adam's ears
    Can it be?
Ballads of six thousand years
    Thrive, thrive;
Songs awaken with the spheres
    Alive.

Mighty songs that miss decay,
    What are they?
Crowds and cities pass away
    Like a day.
Books are out and books are read;
    What are they?
Years will lay them with the dead—
    Sigh, sigh;
Trifles unto nothing wed,
    They die.

Dreamers, mark the honey bee;
    Mark the tree
Where the blue cap "*tootle tee*"
    Sings a glee
Sung to Adam and to Eve—
    Here they be.
When floods covered every bough,
    Noah's ark
Heard that ballad singing now;
    Hark, hark,

"*Tootle tootle tootle tee*"—
    Can it be
Pride and fame must shadows be?
    Come and see—
Every season own her own;
    Bird and bee
Sing creation's music on;
    Nature's glee
Is in every mood and tone
    Eternity.

John Clare

Music

Orpheus with his lute made trees,
        And the mountain-tops that freeze,
Bow themselves when he did sing.
        To his music plants and flowers
Ever sprung: as sun and showers
        There had made a lasting spring.
Everything that heard him play,
        Even the billows of the sea,
Hung their heads, and then lay by.
        In sweet music is such art,
Killing care and grief of heart
        Fall asleep, or, hearing, die.

John Fletcher

Piano

Softly, in the dusk, a woman is singing to me;
Taking me back down the vista of years, till I see
A child sitting under the piano, in the boom of the tingling strings
And pressing the small, poised feet of a mother who smiles as she sings.

In spite of myself, the insidious mastery of song
Betrays me back, till the heart of me weeps to belong
To the old Sunday evenings at home, with winter outside
And hymns in the cosy parlour, the tinkling piano our guide.

So now it is vain for the singer to burst into clamour
With the great black piano appassionato. The glamour
Of childish days is upon me, my manhood is cast
Down in the flood of remembrance, I weep like a child for the past.

D. H. Lawrence

I Am of Ireland

I am of Ireland,
And of the holy land
Of Ireland.

Good sir, pray I thee,
For of saint charity,
Come and dance with me
In Ireland.

Anonymous

To Emilia V—

Music, when soft voices die,
Vibrates in the memory—
Odours, when sweet violets sicken,
Live within the sense they quicken.

Rose leaves, when the rose is dead,
Are heaped for the beloved's bed—
And so thy thoughts, when thou art gone,
Love itself shall slumber on…

Percy Bysshe Shelley

SADNESS
and
HAPPINESS

So, We'll Go No More A-Roving

So, we'll go no more a-roving
    So late into the night,
Though the heart be still as loving,
    And the moon be still as bright.

For the sword outwears its sheath,
    And the soul wears out the breast,
And the heart must pause to breathe,
    And love itself have rest.

Though the night was made for loving,
    And the day returns too soon,
Yet we'll go no more a-roving
    By the light of the moon.

George Gordon, Lord Byron

Spring and Fall

to a young child

Margaret, are you grieving
Over Goldengrove unleaving?
Leaves, like the things of man, you
With your fresh thoughts care for, can you?
Ah! as the heart grows older
It will come to such sights colder
By and by, nor spare a sigh
Though worlds of wanwood leafmeal lie,
And yet you *will* weep and know why.
Now no matter, child, the name:
Sorrow's springs are the same.
Nor mouth had, no nor mind, expressed
What heart heard of, ghost guessed:
It is the blight man was born for,
It is Margaret you mourn for.

Gerard Manley Hopkins

Canadian Boat Song

Listen to me, as when ye heard our father
Sing long ago the song of other shores—
Listen to me, and then in chorus gather
All your deep voices as ye pull your oars:
　　Fair these broad meads—these hoary woods are grand
　　But we are exiles from our fathers' land.

From the lone shieling of the misty island
Mountains divide us, and the waste of seas,
Yet still the blood is strong, the heart is Highland,
And we in dreams behold the Hebrides.

We ne'er shall tread the fancy-haunted valley,
Where 'tween the dark hills creeps the small clear stream,
In arms around the patriarch banner rally,
Nor see the moon on royal tombstones gleam.

When the bold kindred in the time long vanished,
Conquered the soil and fortified the keep—
No seer foretold the children would be banished,
That a degenerate lord might boast his sheep.

Come foreign rage—let Discord burst in slaughter!
O then for clansmen true, and stern claymore,
The hearts that would have given their blood like water,
Beat heavily beyond the Atlantic roar.
　　Fair these broad meads—these hoary woods are grand
　　But we are exiles from our fathers' land.

Anonymous

66

In the Highlands

In the highlands, in the country places,
Where the old plain men have rosy faces,
And the young fair maidens
Quiet eyes;
Where essential silence cheers and blesses,
And for ever in the hill-recesses
Her more lovely music
Broods and dies.

O to mount again where erst I haunted;
Where the old red hills are bird-enchanted,
And the low green meadows
Bright with sward;
And when even dies, the million-tinted,
And the night has come, and planets glinted,
Lo, the valley hollow
Lamp-bestarred!

O to dream, O to awake and wander
There, and with delight to take and render,
Through the trance of silence,
Quiet breath;
Lo! for there, among the flowers and grasses,
Only the mightier movement sounds and passes;
Only winds and rivers,
Life and death.

Robert Louis Stevenson

When in Disgrace With Fortune

When in disgrace with Fortune and men's eyes
I all alone beweep my outcast state,
And trouble deaf heaven with my bootless cries,
And look upon myself and curse my fate,
Wishing me like to one more rich in hope,
Featured like him, like him with friends possessed,
Desiring this man's art, and that man's scope,
With what I most enjoy contented least,
Yet in these thoughts myself almost despising,
Haply I think on thee, and then my state
(Like to the lark at break of day arising
From sullen earth) sings hymns at heaven's gate,
    For thy sweet love remembered such wealth brings,
    That then I scorn to change my state with kings.

William Shakespeare

Piping Down the Valleys Wild

Piping down the valleys wild,
Piping songs of pleasant glee,
On a cloud I saw a child,
And he laughing said to me:

"Pipe a song about a Lamb!"
So I piped with merry chear.
"Piper, pipe that song again;"
So I piped: he wept to hear.

"Drop thy pipe, thy happy pipe;
"Sing thy songs of happy chear:"
So I sung the same again,
While he wept with joy to hear.

"Piper, sit thee down and write
In a book, that all may read."
So he vanish'd from my sight,
And I pluck'd a hollow reed,

And I made a rural pen,
And I stain'd the water clear,
And I wrote my happy songs
Every child may joy to hear.

William Blake

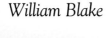

A Lark's Nest

Now's the time for mirth and play,
Saturday's an holiday;
Praise to heav'n unceasing yield,
I've found a lark's nest in the field.

A lark's nest, then your play-mate begs
You'd spare herself and speckled eggs;
Soon she shall ascend and sing
Your praise to th'eternal King.

Christopher Smart

From *The Song of Solomon*

My beloved spake, and said unto me, Rise up, my love, my fair one, and
come away.
For lo, the winter is past, the rain is over, and gone.
The flowers appear on the earth, the time of the singing of birds is come,
and the voice of the turtle is heard in our land.
The fig tree putteth forth her green figs, and the vines with the tender
grape give a good smell.
Arise, my love, my fair one, and come away.

King James Bible

The Swing

How do you like to go up in a swing,
Up in the air so blue?
Oh, I do think it the pleasantest thing
Ever a child can do!

Up in the air and over the wall
Till I can see so wide,
Rivers and trees and cattle and all
Over the countryside—

Till I look down on the garden green,
Down on the roof so brown—
Up in the air I go flying again,
Up in the air and down!

Robert Louis Stevenson

Requiem

Under the wide and starry sky,
Dig the grave and let me lie.
Glad did I live and gladly die,
And I laid me down with a will.

This be the verse you grave for me:
Here he lies where he longed to be;
Home is the sailor, home from the sea,
And the hunter home from the hill.

Robert Louis Stevenson

ABOUT THE POETS

WILLIAM BLAKE
1757–1827

Page 70 Born in London, Blake was a painter and engraver as well as a poet. He illustrated many of his own poems with vivid engravings.

FRANCIS WILLIAM BOURDILLON
1852–1921

Page 16 Bourdillon was an English poet. This is his best known work. The first line is based on a line by the sixteenth-century poet Lyly.

ROBERT BROWNING
1812–89

Pages 32, 60 Browning's poems attracted much attention during his lifetime, including that of fellow poet Elizabeth Barrett. They were married in 1846.

 ### ROBERT BURNS
1759–96

Pages 10, 44 This Scottish poet was very famous during his lifetime for his poems and songs. He worked on a farm in his early years and later, when his writing had brought him wealth, bought his own farm.

GEORGE GORDON, LORD BYRON
1788–1824

Page 64 A romantic figure, very popular during his lifetime, Byron died of fever in Greece, supporting a Greek uprising.

JOHN CLARE
1794–1864

Page 58 Although he had little education, John Clare wrote movingly about the countryside and his feelings of loss and sadness. His life was difficult and often unhappy, but his poems still move us today.

JOHN FLETCHER
1579–1625

Page 60 Known mainly as a playwright, Fletcher was writing in London at the same time as Shakespeare and may have worked with him on some plays.

SIR W. S. GILBERT
1836–1911

Page 30 Gilbert is best known for writing the words in the famous musical partnership with Sir Arthur Sullivan.

THOMAS HARDY
1840–1928
Page 50 This poet and novelist was born in the south-west of England, which appears over and over again in his work.

GERARD MANLEY HOPKINS
1844–89
Page 65 As a young man, Hopkins became a Roman Catholic. Many of his poems have a religious theme. He also experimented with rhythm.

ROBERT JONES
lived around 1600
Page 8 Jones wrote songs for several voices, called madrigals, and simpler airs, such as *Robin Hood*, to be sung to the lute, a stringed instrument.

 JOHN KEATS
1795–1821
Pages 34, 53, 55 Trained as a doctor, Keats died tragically young. "Here lies one whose name was writ in water" is written on his grave.

D. H. LAWRENCE
1885–1930
Page 61 The son of a miner, Lawrence wrote several novels set in the mining area of the English Midlands, as well as others reflecting his many travels abroad.

HENRY WADSWORTH LONGFELLOW
1807–82
Page 38 As well as short poems, this American poet told long stories in verse, such as *Hiawatha*. He visited London in 1842 and stayed with the novelist Charles Dickens.

 ANDREW MARVELL
1621–78
Page 56 Marvell spent the early part of his working life as a tutor to wealthy families. Later, he became an energetic politician and a defender of the poet John Milton.

A. B. PATERSON
1864–1941
Page 42 The famous Australian poem *Waltzing Matilda* has been attributed to this poet, although some people think it was based on an older ballad.

CHRISTINA ROSSETTI
1830–94
Page 11 The poet's Italian father settled in London before her birth.

Her famous brother was the painter and poet Dante Gabriel Rossetti.

 SIR WALTER SCOTT
1771–1832
Page 12 A poet and novelist, Scott celebrated all things Scottish in his work and was very widely read during his lifetime.

WILLIAM SHAKESPEARE
1564–1616
Pages 40, 69 Perhaps the greatest playwright in the English language, Shakespeare also wrote over 150 sonnets—poems of fourteen lines.

PERCY BYSSHE SHELLEY
1792–1822
Page 62 Shelley shocked English society with his beliefs. His later years were spent abroad. His many poems and dramas were all written when he was a young man, for he drowned off the coast of Italy when only thirty years old.

 CHRISTOPHER SMART
1722–71
Page 71 As well as writing poetry, Smart also made translations of the Bible and classical authors.

ROBERT LOUIS STEVENSON
1850–94
Pages 68, 72, 73 A popular writer of stories and poems for children, Stevenson is also known for his novels *Treasure Island*, *Kidnapped* and *The Strange Case of Dr. Jekyll and Mr. Hyde*.

WALT WHITMAN
1819–92
Page 32 Whitman's varied life and experiences in the American Civil War are reflected in his poems, but real fame only came after his death.

OSCAR WILDE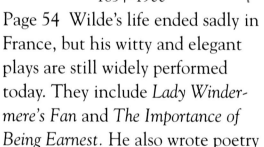
1854–1900
Page 54 Wilde's life ended sadly in France, but his witty and elegant plays are still widely performed today. They include *Lady Winder-mere's Fan* and *The Importance of Being Earnest*. He also wrote poetry and several stories for children.

WILLIAM WORDSWORTH
1770–1850
Page 52 Wordsworth is best known as a poet of nature, who used simple language to express his love for the Lake District in England.

GLOSSARY

a' all
ae one
ain own
alighted got down from his horse
ane one
atweel know well
aught a bairn to me had a child with me
aye always
bairn child
baith both
barton barn
beweep cry about
billabong dead-end water-filled channel
billy can
blude blood
bootless fruitless
brae brow of a hill
braid broad
brake thicket
bukes books
burgess well-to-do citizen
charger war-horse
chear cheer
claymore broadsword
comelie handsome
coolabah tree kind of gum tree
coomb valley
croup hindquarters (of a horse)
dauntless bold
demesne estate
dinna don't
eke also
ere before
erst first
even evening
fa' fall
faem foam
fairlies wonders

fause false
fealty loyalty, trust
fernie ferny
fleet fast
fleurs-de-lys iris-flower pattern appearing
        in heraldry
ford river crossing
frae from
galliard courtly dance
gane gone
gang go
ganging going
gaun going
gied gave
gild gilded
gin if
goud gold
grave carve
grumly fierce-looking
gude good
hae have
halcyon calm
haply by chance
het hot
hoary ancient
hooly gently
ilka every
jow stroke
jumbuck sheep
keep strongest part of castle
ken know, knowledge
kerchers kerchiefs, head-dresses
knaves rogues
knicht knight
larn learn
lay (a ghost) put a ghost to rest
lillie leven lovely glade
lily wean lovely little one

mantel cloak
maun must
meads meadows
mither mother
mony many
muckle great
na not
ne'er never
nigh nearly
nourrice, nourris nurse
o' of
o'er over
omnibus horsedrawn bus
pall gloomy covering
putteth puts
quaffed drank
quid piece of tobacco being chewed
quo' said
quoth said
rade rode
reft torn
saft soft
sall shall
scaur cliff
scule school
shew show
shieling hut on grazing land
shouthers shoulders
sic such
sich such
sie sea
silkie seal
sma' thin
spake spoke
squatter sheepstation owner

stane stone
staps steps
steeds horses
stude stood
Sule Skerrie Seal Reef
swagman tramp carrying a swag or bundle
sward grass
ta'en taken
tett lock of hair of mane
thees thighs
thou you
thu you
tucker-bag food bag
turtle turtle dove
twa two
unceasing without stopping
vair fur
wae woe
waged gambled
waltzing Matilda carrying a swag
wan pale
weel well
wessel vessel, ship
wha's aucht thae? whose are those?
whare? where?
what way? why?
wi' with
wight creature
wiss wish
wittles food
wive marry
wrought made
ye you
yon yonder

INDEX OF TITLES AND FIRST LINES

A Birthday   11
A Lark's Nest   71
A New Courtly Sonnet of the Lady
    Greensleeves   14
A Red, Red Rose   10
A Strange Visitor   47
A thing of beauty is a joy for ever   55
A Thing of Beauty   55
A wife was sitting at her reel ae night   47
Alas, my Love! ye do me wrong   14
An earthly nourris sits and sings   24
An omnibus across the bridge   54

Bonny Barbara Allan   22

Canadian Boat Song   66
Children   38
Christmas Eve, and twelve of the
    clock   50
Come to me, O ye children!   38

Earth has nothing to show more fair   52

From The Garden   56
From The Song of Solomon   71

How do you like to go up in a swing   72

I Am of Ireland   62
I am of Ireland   62
In the Highlands   68
In the highlands, in the country places   68
It was in and about the Martinmas
    time   22

Jemima   33
John Barleycorn   44

Listen to me, as when ye heard our
    father   66
Lochinvar   12

Margaret, are you grieving   65
Much have I travell'd in the realms
    of gold   53
Music   60
Music, when soft voices die   62
My beloved spake, and said unto me,
    Rise up, my love, my fair one, and
    come away   71
My heart is like a singing bird   11
My love is like a red, red rose   10

Now's the time for mirth and play   71

"O whare are ye gaun?"   36
O, young Lochinvar is come out of
    the west   12
On First Looking into Chapman's
    Homer   53
Once a jolly swagman camped by a
    billabong   42
Orpheus with his lute made trees   60

Piano   61
Piping down the valleys wild   70
Piping Down the Valleys Wild   70

Requiem   73

So, We'll Go No More A-Roving   64
So, we'll go no more a-roving   64
Softly, in the dusk, a woman is singing
    to me   61
Song's Eternity   58

Spring and Fall  65
Symphony in Yellow 54

The False Knight and the Wee Boy 36
The Ghost's Song 43
The Great Silkie of Sule Skerrie 24
The Night Has a Thousand Eyes 16
The night has a thousand eyes 16
The Oxen 50
The Swing 72
The Yarn of the Nancy Bell 26
There was a little girl, and she wore
   a little curl 33
There Was a Naughty Boy 34
There was a naughty boy 34
There was three Kings into the east 44
Thomas the Rhymer 18
To Emilia V— 62
True Thomas lay o'er yond grassy bank 18

'Twas on the shores that round our
   coast 26

Under the wide and starry sky 73
Upon Westminster Bridge 52

Wae's me! wae's me! 43
Waltzing Matilda 42
What am I after all but a child, pleas'd
   with the sound of my own name?
   repeating it over and over 32
What Am I After All 32
What is song's eternity? 58
What wondrous life in this I lead! 56
When in disgrace with fortune and
   men's eyes 69
When in Disgrace With Fortune 69
When That I Was and a Little Tiny Boy 40
When that I was and a little tiny boy 40